YOU'D NEED ONE OF THEM NEUTRON MICROSCOPES, DOMMER. IT'S IDENTICAL DOWN TO BEN FRANKLIN'S STUBBLE.

ANYBODY GOT A PROBLEM WITH THAT?

KKRASSH

HEY!

WHAT?

THE BAT!

BLAM BLAM

2

CHUCKIE SOL...

BATMAN!

BLAM BLAM BLAM

CLICK CLICK

YOUR ANGEL OF DEATH AWAITS.

YOU AIN'T THE BATMAN!

WH- WHO ARE YOU? WHADDAYA WANT?

I WANT YOU, CHUCKIE BOY.

KRAAASSSHH

3

HOW MANY TIMES, GOTHAM? HOW MANY TIMES ARE WE GOING TO LET BATMAN CROSS THE LINE?

I'M *SORRY*, COUNCILMAN -- YOU CAN'T BLAME BATMAN FOR CHUCKIE SOL'S DEATH.

WHY *NOT* ?!

HE'S A *LOOSE CANNON*, COMMISSIONER. A *LOT* OF PEOPLE THINK BATMAN'S AS UNSTABLE AS THE CROOKS HE BRINGS IN.

WHAT KIND OF CITY ARE WE RUNNING WHEN WE DEPEND ON THE SUPPORT OF A POTENTIAL MADMAN ?!

SUCH ROT, SIR. WHY, YOU'RE THE VERY *MODEL* OF SANITY.

OH, BY THE WAY, I'VE PRESSED YOUR TIGHTS AND PUT AWAY YOUR EXPLODING GAS BALLS.

THANK YOU, ALFRED.

MIGHT ONE INQUIRE WHAT THIS IS?

A PIECE OF SAFETY GLASS I FOUND AT THE SCENE OF THE ACCIDENT. THERE'S A CHEMICAL RESIDUE BAKED ONTO IT -- SOME KIND OF DENSE LONG-CHAIN POLYMER.

OF *COURSE.*

I SHOULD BE LANDING ANY MINUTE.

IT'LL BE GOOD TO SEE YOU AGAIN, ARTHUR.

YOU, TOO. AND DON'T YOU WORRY ABOUT THOSE OLD FAMILY FINANCES. DON'T FORGET, YOU'VE GOT A BIG-TIME CITY COUNCILMAN ON YOUR SIDE.

CAN'T BELIEVE IT'S BEEN TEN YEARS.

THINKING OF LOOKING UP SOME OLD FRIENDS?

OH, ARTHUR, DON'T START THAT AGAIN. HE'S ANCIENT HISTORY.

THAT'S ENCOURAGING. THEN I'LL SEE YOU SOON.

LADIES AND GENTLEMEN, PLEASE FASTEN YOUR SEAT BELTS. WE'RE ABOUT TO MAKE OUR DESCENT INTO GOTHAM CITY.

COME *ON*, BRUCE. ALL ALONE IN THIS BIG MANSION. HAVEN'T YOU EVER THOUGHT ABOUT MARRIAGE, EVEN *ONCE*?

OH, NEVER SAY THE "M" WORD IN FRONT OF BRUCE. IT MAKES HIM *NERVOUS.*

I'D WATCH OUT FOR BRUCIE, IF I WERE YOU, GIRLS. FIRST HE WINES AND DINES YOU, MAKES YOU THINK YOU'RE THE ONLY WOMAN HE'S EVER BEEN INTERESTED IN, AND JUST WHEN YOU'RE WONDERING WHERE TO REGISTER THE CHINA...

... HE FORGETS YOUR PHONE NUMBER. *THAT'S* BRUCE WAYNE'S STYLE.

REALLY, BRUCE, IT'S ALMOST AS IF YOU PICK THEM BECAUSE YOU *KNOW* THERE'S NO CHANCE FOR A SERIOUS RELATIONSHIP.

COUNCILMAN REEVES.

AT LEAST SINCE THAT ONE GIRL... WHAT WAS HER NAME? ANNE... ANDI... *ANDREA.*

8

"YOU REMEMBER, BRUCE. ANDREA BEAUMONT."

WAYNE

KNOW WHO ELSE IS HERE? BRUCE WAYNE. *YOU* KNOW. WAYNE ENTERPRISES?

I'VE SEEN HIM ON CAMPUS. *VERY* MOODY. CUTE, THOUGH. I --

YES?

I HEARD MY NAME. I THOUGHT... WHO ARE YOU TALKING TO?

MY MOTHER.

IN LOVING MEMORY
VICTORIA BEAUMONT

OH. I DIDN'T MEAN TO...

THAT'S OKAY. WE'RE DONE. MOM DOESN'T HAVE MUCH TO SAY TODAY.

MUCH TO SAY...?

WHEN I TALK TO HER OUT LOUD, I CAN IMAGINE HOW SHE'D REPLY. I CAN *HEAR* HER, LIKE SHE'S RIGHT THERE.

I TALKED TO MY PARENTS. ONCE.

IN LOVING MEMORY

OOOH, A MAN OF *MYSTERY.*

WHAT DID YOU SAY?

I MADE A VOW. A *SECRET* ONE.

ANDREA BEAUMONT.

BRUCE WAYNE.

I KNOW. THE BOY BILLIONAIRE. SO, TELL ME...

WITH ALL THAT MONEY AND POWER, HOW COME YOU ALWAYS LOOK LIKE YOU WANT TO JUMP OFF A CLIFF?

WHY SHOULD YOU CARE?

I DON'T. MY MOTHER WAS ASKING.

NOW!

YAAAAH!

GET HIM!

⑬

Gotham Gazette

MYSTERIOUS VIGILANTE REPELS BANDITS

I READ ABOUT YOUR ANONYMOUS EXPLOITS THIS MORNING AND I MUST SAY...

...ARE YOU SURE YOU WON'T RECONSIDER RUGBY?

SORRY, ALFRED, BUT "THE PLAN" IS WORKING. I HAD THE EDGE. I COULD *FEEL* IT. THERE WAS ONLY ONE THING WRONG.

THEY WEREN'T *AFRAID* OF ME. I'VE GOT TO STRIKE FEAR IN THEM FROM THE START.

PARDON, MASTER BRUCE, BUT WE MAY WANT TO POSTPONE THE SHOP TALK AS IT WERE. I BELIEVE YOU HAVE A VISITOR.

HI.

IT'S BEEN THREE DAYS SINCE WE MET AND STILL NO CALLS. I FIGURED YOU MUST BE DEAD OR SOMETHING.

YOU EXPECT EVERY GUY YOU MEET TO CALL YOU UP?

THE ONES THAT ARE SMART ENOUGH TO DIAL A PHONE.

WHAT IS THAT YOU'RE DOING?

YOU WOULDN'T UNDERSTAND. IT'S A MARTIAL ART FROM OKINAWA. THE MOVES REQUIRE COMPLETE CONCENTRATION--

16

17

THERE APPEARS TO BE SOME CHEMICAL RESIDUE ON THE LAWN. IT COULD MATCH THE TRACES I FOUND ON THE GLASS. NOT MUCH, BUT IT'S BEEN THAT KIND OF DAY.

YOU'D THINK THEY COULD AFFORD A WEED-EATER. SORRY, MOM, BUT THE WHOLE WORLD'S GOING TO--

BRUCE!

...SO I'M HAVING THE BANKER CUT THROUGH SOME RED TAPE. HE SAYS HE CAN ROLL YOUR MONEY INTO A HIGHER-YIELD ACCOUNT.

AMOUNT? WHAT AMOUNT?

I SAID "ACCOUNT."

I'M SORRY. I WAS JUST... REMINISCING.

MENU

REMEMBER THIS PLACE?

SURE. YOU, ME AND DADDY USED TO COME HERE ALL THE TIME.

HOW *IS* THE OLD GUY? YOU'RE STILL CLOSE, AREN'T YOU?

CLOSER THAN EVER.

I'M SORRY HE COULDN'T MAKE IT INTO TOWN THIS TIME.

BUT THEN I'VE ALWAYS WISHED I COULD HAVE SOME TIME ALONE WITH YOU.

WELL... WHO KNOWS WHAT THE FUTURE MIGHT BRING?

WELCOME TO A DREAM OF THE FUTURE. A BRIGHT TOMORROW FILLED WITH HOPE AND PROMISE FOR ALL MANKIND.

THIS IS A VISION OF THE SHIMMERING UTOPIA WHERE WE WILL ALL SPEND THE REST OF OUR LIVES.

♫ OUR DREAMS ARE SHINING BRIGHT. GLORY AND WONDER SURROUND US, A NEW TOMORROW IS IN SIGHT. ♫

♫ WE'LL WELCOME IN A BRAND-NEW DAY! FORWARD, GOTHAM, TO THE FUTURE, THE FUTURE STARTS TODAY. ♫

DO YOU THINK WE'LL REALLY SEE ANY OF THIS IN OUR LIFETIME?

BRUCE?

HUH?

OH, I'M SORRY, ANDI. MY MIND WAS ON... SOMETHING ELSE...

LIKE WHAT?

OH, JUST... PLANS, FOR THE FUTURE. YOU KNOW...

EXIT

GIANT TURBIN

NO, I DON'T. WHEN WAS THE LAST TIME YOU TALKED TO ME ABOUT YOUR PLANS?

Y'KNOW, DAD'S BEEN WANTING TO MEET YOU. I TOLD HIM YOU'RE NOT UP TO IT YET.

I CAN MEET HIM.

GREAT! I'LL CALL HIM RIGHT NOW!

YOU SURE ABOUT THIS?

SURE I'M SURE.

WHAT THE HECK AM I DOING, ALFRED? THIS ISN'T PART OF THE PLAN!

I MUST BE GOING NUTS.

IF I MAY BE SO BOLD, MASTER BRUCE--I'D SAY QUITE THE REVERSE.

24

SIR, IF YOU COULD JUST GO OVER THESE...

KNOCK, KNOCK

WELL, THIS IS A MOST PLEASANT INTERRUPTION.

AT LAST I MEET THE ELUSIVE BRUCE WAYNE.

NICE TO MEET YOU, SIR.

"SIR"? DON'T BE SO FORMAL, BRUCE. ANDREA'S TOLD ME SO MUCH ABOUT YOU, I FEEL LIKE WE'RE PRACTICALLY FAMILY.

DADDY...

>AHEM<

OH, I'M SORRY. THIS IS ARTHUR REEVES, ONE OF THE HOT YOUNG TURKS FROM MY LEGAL DEPARTMENT.

HE'S SOMEONE YOU SHOULD GET TO KNOW.

I HOPE WE'RE NOT INTERRUPTING ANYTHING.

NOT AT ALL. I'M NEVER TOO BUSY FOR MY ANDI, AND HER FRIENDS.

I TELL YOU, BRUCE, ALL THE MONEY IN THE WORLD MEANS LITTLE, IF YOU DON'T HAVE LOVED ONES TO SHARE IT WITH. NOTHING'S MORE IMPORTANT THAN FAMILY.

YES, MR. BEAUMONT.

25

CALL ME CARL.

EXCUSE ME, SIR...

...BUT THERE'S A MISTER VALESTRA HERE TO SEE YOU. HE *SAYS* HE HAS AN APPOINTMENT.

IF MISTER VALESTRA SAYS HE HAS AN APPOINTMENT, VIRGINIA...

...THEN MISTER VALESTRA HAS AN APPOINTMENT.

THAT'S WHAT I LIKE ABOUT YOUR POP, KIDDO--

--HE KNOWS HIS PRIORITIES.

IS MY SHIRT TOO BIG, OR IS THAT MY FLESH CRAWLING?

I HEAR MISTER VALESTRA HAS THAT EFFECT ON PEOPLE SOMETIMES.

C'MON, BRUCE. DAD JUST COUNTS THEIR MONEY. THEY DON'T TELL HIM WHERE IT COMES FROM.

IT'S NOT YOUR FATHER, ANDI, IT'S...

I *SAID,* HAND OVER THE CASH BOX, MAN!

WHAT DO YOU EXPECT ME TO DO, JUST STAND HERE?

PLEASE! IT'S ALL I GOT!

STAY PUT. THIS COULD GET SERIOUS.

BRUCE, NO! DON'T!

HEY!

HAHAHA

JUST COME BACK TO ME IN ONE PIECE. *PLEASE.*

WHAM

OOOOM

27

VROO

JUST COME BACK TO ME IN ONE PIECE.

BETTER HAVE YOUR INSURANCE PAID UP, SUCKER!

KRAKK

C'MON, LET ME HAVE A LOOK AT YOU...

ANDREA, PLEASE...

BRUCE! ARE YOU ALL RIGHT?

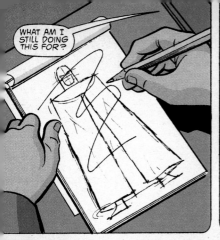

WHAT AM I STILL DOING THIS FOR?

IT'S GOTTA BE ONE OR THE OTHER-- I CAN'T HAVE IT BOTH WAYS. I CAN'T PUT MYSELF ON THE LINE AS LONG AS THERE'S SOMEONE WAITING FOR ME TO COME HOME.

MISS BEAUMONT WOULD BE GLAD TO KNOW YOU FEEL THAT WAY, MASTER BRUCE.

SHE'S HOLDING ON LINE ONE.

ALFRED, I CAN'T. NOT NOW.

WHAT SHALL I SAY?

I DON'T KNOW. I JUST DON'T KNOW.

THUD

IT DOESN'T MEAN I DON'T CARE ANYMORE. I *DON'T* WANT TO LET YOU DOWN -- HONEST. BUT... BUT...

...IT JUST DOESN'T HURT SO BAD ANYMORE. YOU CAN UNDERSTAND THAT, CAN'T YOU?

I KNOW I MADE A PROMISE, BUT I DIDN'T SEE THIS COMING. I DIDN'T COUNT ON BEING HAPPY.

PLEASE. TELL ME THAT IT'S OKAY.

WAYNE

MAYBE THEY ALREADY HAVE.

MAYBE THEY *SENT* ME.

GET IN.

ALL I WANT TO KNOW IS, IS IT TRUE? IS THE BATMAN REALLY HITTING OUR PEOPLE?

WE HAVE EYEWITNESSES.

BEAUTIFUL. THAT'S JUST BEAUTIFUL. WHY? HE NEVER LEANED ON US BEFORE. I'M TOO OLD FOR THIS!

I SUPPOSE YOU COULD DEMAND POLICE PROTECTION.

WHAT ARE YOU, A COMEDIAN? THIS IS THE BATMAN WE'RE TALKING ABOUT HERE. A *FREAK* JOB... HE'LL CRUCIFY ME...

PULL OVER.

IT'S NOT VERY HEALTHY IN HERE.

>WHEEZE< >COUGH< >COUGH<

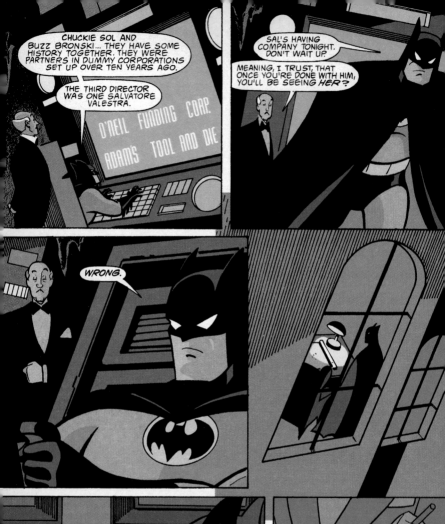

CHUCKIE SOL AND BUZZ BRONSKI... THEY HAVE SOME HISTORY TOGETHER. THEY WERE PARTNERS IN DUMMY CORPORATIONS SET UP OVER TEN YEARS AGO.

THE THIRD DIRECTOR WAS ONE SALVATORE VALESTRA.

O'NEIL FUNDING CORP.

ADAMS TOOL AND DIE

SAL'S HAVING COMPANY TONIGHT. DON'T WAIT UP.

MEANING, I TRUST, THAT ONCE YOU'RE DONE WITH HIM, YOU'LL BE SEEING *HER*?

WRONG.

"...YOU KNOW HOW MUCH I'VE ALWAYS WANTED TO SEE EUROPE, BRUCE. AND DAD HAS BUSINESS THERE NEXT WEEK..."

UH-OH.

LOOKS LIKE DAD'S GOT COMPANY--

--BUSINESS-TYPE COMPANY.

HE DOESN'T USUALLY SEE CLIENTS HERE AT HOME. AT LEAST NOT AT THIS HOUR.

MAYBE WE SHOULD WAIT TILL TOMORROW BEFORE WE GIVE HIM THE GOOD NEWS.

MAYBE.

GOODNIGHT, BRUCE. ALFRED.

WOOF!

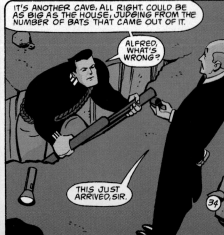

IT'S ANOTHER CAVE, ALL RIGHT. COULD BE AS BIG AS THE HOUSE, JUDGING FROM THE NUMBER OF BATS THAT CAME OUT OF IT.

ALFRED, WHAT'S WRONG?

THIS JUST ARRIVED, SIR.

YOU HAVE AN EXCELLENT SENSE OF TIMING.

IT WAS ALL OVER TV-- I HAD TO DO SOMETHING.

I'M GRATEFUL, OF COURSE.

BUT I STILL NEED TO KNOW WHY YOU'RE NOT TELLING ME THE TRUTH ABOUT YOUR FATHER.

WELL, I SUPPOSE THE WORLD'S GREATEST DETECTIVE WILL FIND OUT EVENTUALLY. YOU REMEMBER DADDY WAS HAVING A MEETING THAT NIGHT WITH HIS "PARTNERS"...

IT AIN'T RIGHT, CARL. YOU'VE TAKEN WHAT'S OURS. YOU'RE GOING TO PAY ONE WAY OR ANOTHER.

LEAVE HIM ALONE!

I'M SORRY YOU HAD TO SEE THIS, MS. BEAUMONT.

DON'T! PLEASE, SAL-- GIVE ME ONE MORE DAY! I SWEAR I'LL GET THE MONEY!

CONVINCE ME.

THIS TIME TOMORROW. ON MY MOTHER'S GRAVE. AS SOON AS THE EUROPEAN BANKS OPEN I'LL HAVE THE WHOLE AMOUNT WIRED TO YOU.

TWENTY-FOUR HOURS. THIS TIME TOMORROW, WE'LL HAVE THE MONEY-- OR I'LL HAVE YOUR HEART IN MY HAND.

LET'S GO, BOYS.

QUICKLY, ANDREA-- PACK A SUITCASE. WE'VE GOT TO GET TO THE AIRPORT *NOW.*

WHAT?! BUT YOU SAID YOU'D HAVE THE MONEY--

IT'S NOT THAT SIMPLE. THE MONEY'S TIED UP IN INVESTMENTS. COULD TAKE WEEKS TO FREE IT UP.

BUT I CAN'T LEAVE! BRUCE PROPOSED TO ME-- WE'RE GOING TO GET MARRIED!

LISTEN TO ME! I JUST USED UP THE LAST SHRED OF PITY SAL VALESTRA HAS! IF I DON'T PAY HIM *BACK* WITHIN TWENTY-FOUR HOURS, THEY'LL FIND US AND THEY WILL KILL US BOTH!

HOW-- WHY DID YOU DO THIS, DAD? WHY'D YOU GET INVOLVED WITH THOSE PEOPLE...?

I'M SORRY, ANDI. I-- JUST WANTED A CHANCE FOR YOU-- I--

I'LL GET YOU OUT OF THIS. SOMEHOW WE'LL BE FREE OF THOSE GUYS, WHATEVER IT TAKES. THAT'S A PROMISE.

"WE HID ALL OVER EUROPE. EVENTUALLY SETTLED ON THE MEDITERRANEAN COAST. DAD WAS ABLE TO PARLAY THE MONEY HE EMBEZZLED INTO A FORTUNE."

FINALLY HE HAD ENOUGH TO PAY THEM BACK--OR SO HE THOUGHT. THEY WANTED INTEREST... COMPOUNDED IN *BLOOD.*

HE HAD TO FIND ANOTHER WAY.

THE MAN IN THE COSTUME -- YOUR FATHER?

HE SAID HE'D GET THEM, SOMEHOW. WHEN I HEARD ABOUT CHUCKIE SOL... WELL, I HAD TO COME BACK. TO FIND HIM. TO STOP HIM.

I'M SORRY, BRUCE. THAT'S TWICE NOW I'VE COME INTO YOUR LIFE AND SCREWED IT UP.

I'D LIKE TO THINK WE CAN MAKE IT WORK THIS TIME. BUT YOU KNOW IT'S GOING TO COME DOWN BETWEEN ME AND YOUR FATHER.

DADDY DOESN'T MATTER ANYMORE.

IT'S SO GOOD TO SEE YOU AND MISS BEAUMONT TOGETHER AGAIN.

MIGHT ONE ASK WHAT THIS BODES FOR YOUR ALTER EGO?

I'M NOT SURE, ALFRED. SO MUCH HAS CHANGED...

YOU STILL LOVE EACH OTHER. THAT MUCH, AT LEAST, HAS NOT CHANGED.

IT'S TRUE-- I LOVE HER. MAYBE... AFTER THIS IS SETTLED...

... MAYBE THEN...

IS SOMETHING WRONG?

MAYBE...

OH, NO.

JOKER.

HAHAHA

FOUR PRECINCTS ON BATMAN'S HEELS AND HE STILL GOT AWAY! UNBELIEVABLE!

TSK! TSK! AND TO THINK OUR TAX MONEY GOES TO PAY THOSE JERKS!

YOU!

THAT'S RIGHT, ARTIE. BRING IN THE PRESS, WHY DON'TCHA?

WHAT A PHOTO OP! THE COUNCILMAN AND HIS WACKY PAL.

YOU'RE NO FRIEND OF MINE.

OH, ARTIE! I'M CRUSHED! HOW THE HIGH AND MIGHTY FORGET.

DON'TCHA REMEMBER? YOU, ME, SALLIE AND THE GANG?

I NEVER MET THEM OR YOU. I WORKED FOR BEAUMONT. I DIDN'T KNOW WHAT HE WAS DOING.

OH, BUT YOU KNEW ABOUT IT AFTERWARDS...

... AND PUT IT TO GOOD USE, EH?

WHAT DO YOU WANT?

TO FIND OUT WHO'S ICED THE OLD GANG.

HAVEN'T YOU READ THE PAPERS? IT'S BATMAN.

WRONG! IT AIN'T THE BAT. NOPE, NOPE, NOPE.

I'VE *SEEN* THE GUY.

48

YOU'RE SAYING IT'S SOMEONE ELSE?

YEAH. SOMEONE WHO WOULDN'T MIND SEEING OUR OLD PALS OUT OF THE WAY.

MAYBE--GULP, SOB--ME, TOO.

THAT'S WHEN I THOUGHT ABOUT YOU, ARTURO. AN IMPORTANT, UPSTANDING GUY LIKE YOU COULD FIND IT AWKWARD IF CERTAIN SECRETS WERE REVEALED ABOUT HIS PAST.

WAIT, YOU'RE NOT SAYING THAT I ...

MISTER REEVES? MISS BEAUMONT ON THE LINE.

BEAUMONT? NOT THE BABE?

OH, YOU DEVIL, YOU.

ARTHUR?

HELLO, ANDREA. WE'RE STILL ON FOR LUNCH, RIGHT?

I'M SORRY, I GOT HUNG UP. I'LL EXPLAIN EVERYTHING TONIGHT, OKAY?

ALL RIGHT. I'LL SEE YOU THEN.

NOW AIN'T THAT A CO-INKY-DINK? WE'RE TALKIN' ABOUT THE OLD MAN, AND THE SPAWN OF HIS LOINS JUST HAPPENS TO CALL!

MAKES YOU WANT TO LAUGH, DOESN'T IT, ARTIE?

49

COUNCILMAN, PLEASE! YOU'VE GOT TO GET CONTROL OF YOURSELF!

HAHAHA HAHA HAHAHA HA

I'M...HA HA HA... TRYING, FOR GOD'S SAKE!

THERE. THAT SHOULD RELAX YOU ENOUGH FOR THE TOXIN TO RUN ITS COURSE. NOW, TRY TO STAY CALM.

OKAY, OKAY...

OH, N-NO.

WHY DID THE JOKER MEET WITH YOU?

IT HAS TO DO WITH THE GANGSTER MURDERS, DOESN'T IT? HE THINKS YOU'RE INVOLVED. WHY?!

I...HEE HEE... I DON'T KNOW.

THAT'S NOT THE ANSWER I WANT.

B-BEAUMONT NEEDED ME TO HELP HIM AND HIS KID GET OUT OF TOWN. HE KEPT IN TOUCH.

50

WHEN WAS THE LAST TIME YOU SPOKE TO HIM?

YEARS AGO... *HEE HEE*... MY FIRST ELECTION CAMPAIGN. I WAS RUNNING OUT OF MONEY AND... *HA HA HA*... ASKED BEAUMONT FOR HELP? HE SAID NO.

SO YOU SOLD HIM TO THE MOB.

I WAS BROKE! *HA!* DESPERATE! *HA HA!* THEY SAID ALL THEY WANTED... *HA HA*... WAS THEIR MONEY BACK!

HA HA HAHAHA

RING-RING

HELL-OOO... ANYBODY HOME?

LISTEN, BOOPSIE-- EVEN THOUGH YOU NEVER CALL AND NEVER WRITE, I STILL GOT A SOFT SPOT FOR YOU. SO I'M SENDING YOU A FEW GIFTS--*AIR* MAIL.

OH, BY THE WAY-- I WOULDN'T RECOMMEND JUMPING OUT THE WINDOW *THIS* TIME. TA-TA, TOOTS!

51

WELL, HAZE, GUESS IT'S TIME TO CALL IT A NIGHT.

WHADDAYA SAY, HON? FEELING THE OL' ELECTRICITY TONIGHT?

JOKER. YOUR ANGEL OF DEATH AWAITS.

SO YOU FIGURED IT OUT.

GOTTA HAND IT TO YOU-- NICE SCHEME. COSTUME'S A BIT THEATRICAL, BUT HEY, WHO AM I TO TALK?

I'M IMPRESSED, LADY. YOU'RE HARDER TO KILL THAN A COCKROACH ON STEROIDS.

>KAFF! >KAFF!

CUTE. VERY CUTE.

BUT I CAN BLOW SMOKE TOO, TOOTS.

53

WHERE--?

HOW 'BOUT A LITTLE *PICK-ME-UP*?

WELL, IF IT ISN'T *SMOKEY THE BABE*-- JUST IN TIME TO MEET HER BIGGEST *FAN!*

VROOM

BY-AWHOOOOM

I COULDN'T SAVE HER, ALFRED.

I DON'T THINK SHE WANTED TO BE SAVED, SIR.

VENGEANCE BLACKENS THE SOUL, BRUCE. I ALWAYS FEARED YOU WOULD BECOME THAT WHICH YOU FOUGHT AGAINST.

YOU WALK THE EDGE OF THAT ABYSS EVERY NIGHT. BUT YOU HAVEN'T FALLEN IN. AND I THANK HEAVEN FOR THAT.

BUT ANDREA FELL INTO THAT PIT YEARS AGO. AND NO ONE-- NOT EVEN YOU-- COULD HAVE PULLED HER OUT.

End

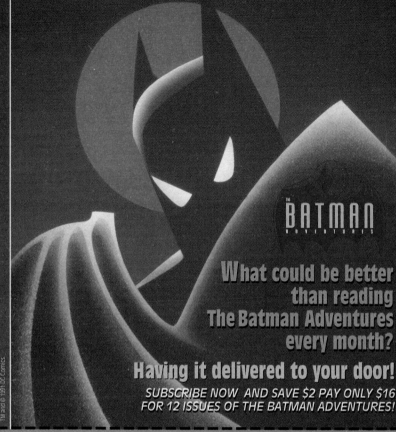